BARTMAN™
THE BEST OF THE BEST!

TITAN BOOKS

TO THE LOVING MEMORY OF *SNOWBALL I:*
YOUR SECRET IDENTITY IS SAFE WITH US .

BARTMAN: THE BEST OF THE BEST. Copyright ©1994 & 1995 by
Bongo Entertainment, Inc. All rights reserved.

Published In The UK by Titan Books, a division of Titan Publishing Group, 144
Southwark St., London SE1 0UP, under license from Bongo Entertainment, Inc.

FIRST EDITION
MARCH 1997
ISBN 1-85286-820-1

8 10 9

Publisher: MATT GROENING
Managing Editor: JASON GRODE
Art Director/Editor: BILL MORRISON
Book Design: MARILYN FRANDSEN
Legal Guardian: SUSAN GRODE
Contributing Artists:
BILL MORRISON, TIM BAVINGTON, PHIL ORTIZ, LUIS ESCOBAR,
STEPHANIE GLADDEN, STEVE VANCE, CINDY VANCE, NATHAN KANE
Contributing Writers:
BILL MORRISON, ANDREW GOTTLIEB, GARY GLASBERG, STEVE VANCE

PRINTED IN SPAIN

CONTENTS

BARTMAN: AN INTRODUCTION

Once in a generation, a modest, unheralded book comes along that speaks from the heart to the deep concerns we all share about our lives. Such a book provides a beacon, a guide, a call to arms, for all who come into contact with it. Sure, it may be packaged between flimsy soft covers and filled with gaudy, colorful illustrations, but that is part of the book's unassuming message. Approaching a book like this with an open mind can only make the world seem even more miraculous, and all but the most casual reader cannot fail to be moved, changed, or filled with a new determination to live life with a heightened awareness. That is simply what happens when reading a book that is so obviously a contemporary classic. This is not that book. This is just a mess of comics. Enjoy!

MATT GROENING
Bongo Comics Group

BARTMAN'S BOTTOM 40

1. BULLIES WITH MEGA-STRENGTH SUPERPOWERS.
2. PARENTS WHO TELL THEIR FRIENDS ABOUT YOUR "CUTE LITTLE COSTUME."
3. SCHOOL NIGHTS.
4. LEARNING THE HARD WAY THAT MAN WAS NOT MEANT TO FLY.
5. SIDEKICKS THAT CAN'T STAY UP PAST NINE O' CLOCK.
6. USING ALLOWANCE TO PAY OFF ANONYMOUS TIP-STERS.
7. FORGETTING THAT THE MOBSTERS AND THE MAYOR DRIVE BLACK LIMOS.
8. THE FINE LINE BETWEEN SUPERHERO AND PSYCHO-VIGILANTE.
9. SLIDING DOWN THE BARTPOLE IN SHORTS.
10. SLICK HOLLYWOOD TYPES THAT TRY TO EXPLOIT YOUR GOOD NAME.
11. THE UNIVERSE IMPLODING UPON ITSELF AND RESTARTING AGAIN WITH SUBTLE CHANGES.
12. CHRONIC COWL-HEAD.
13. HAVING HOMEWORK TO DO BEFORE GOING OUT AND BUSTIN' HEADS.
14. SHARPENING THE GIANT PENCIL IN THE BARTCAVE.
15. POLICE CHIEFS THAT ONLY GIVE YOU 24 HOURS TO CRACK THE CASE.
16. HOUSEBOY'S LACTOSE INTOLERANCE.
17. CONTRACTING TMJ FROM ALL THAT TEETH GRITTING.
18. PSYCHOTIC VILLAINS THAT DON'T USE DEODORANT.
19. BARTDOG'S BOUT WITH COMPULSIVE TAIL CHASING.
20. THE BARTCAVE'S PERSISTENT MILDEW.
21. MANIAC BEEF JERKY MONSTERS FROM DIMENSION Q.
22. GETTING CAUGHT SOLILOQUIZING.
23. CAPE-BURN.
24. DEFECTIVE GRAPPLING HOOKS.
25. CURIOUS SISTERS SEARCHING FOR BLACKMAIL MATERIAL.
26. COMIC BOOK SHOPS THAT ARE CLOSED ON SUNDAY.
27. SELF-CENTERED REPORTERS.
28. POORLY PAVED STREETS AND SIDEWALKS.
29. BAD GUYS WHO DON'T USE OLD WAREHOUSES OR CASTLES FOR HIDEOUTS.
30. ANY USE OF THE WORD "TECHNO."
31. SENSES-SHATTERING ADVENTURES NOT BEING AS SENSES-SHATTERING AS THE GOOD OLD DAYS.
32. THE OBVIOUS MERCHANDISING PLOY IN THE "NEW LOOK" RADIOACTIVE MAN ADVENTURES TELEVISION SHOW.
33. LAX SECURITY AT THE PEN WHERE THEY SEND COSTUMED SUPER-VILLAINS.
34. THE CRIMINAL MENACE NAMED SIDESHOW BOB.
35. MISJUDGING THE DISTANCE BETWEEN THE WINDOW AND THE TREE.
36. HOUSEBOY'S STASH OF MALIBU STACEY COMICS.
37. A LIFETIME OF RADIATION EXPOSURE, YET NO COOL POWERS.
38. "INTIMIDATING VOICE" IS JUST NOT INTIMIDATING.
39. BEING A STREET FIGHTING MAN IN A TOWN FULL OF SIDEWALKS.
40. TAKING A BITE OUT OF CRIME AND GETTING IT STUCK BETWEEN YOUR TEETH.

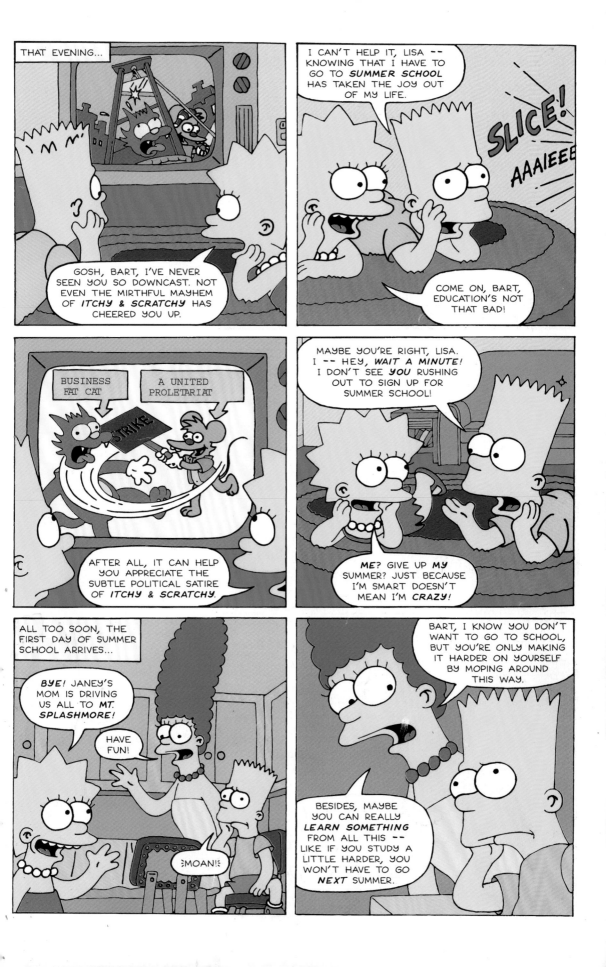

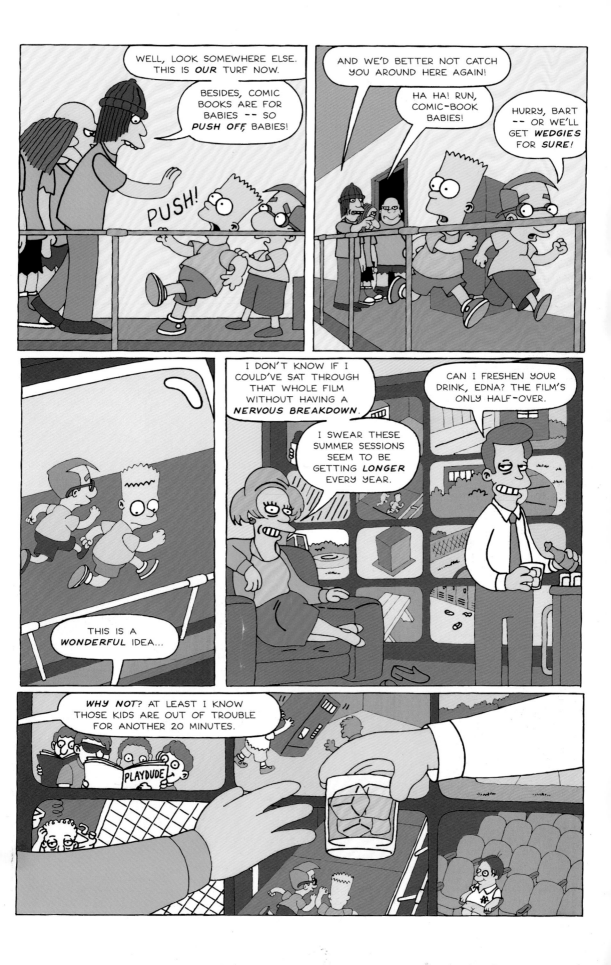

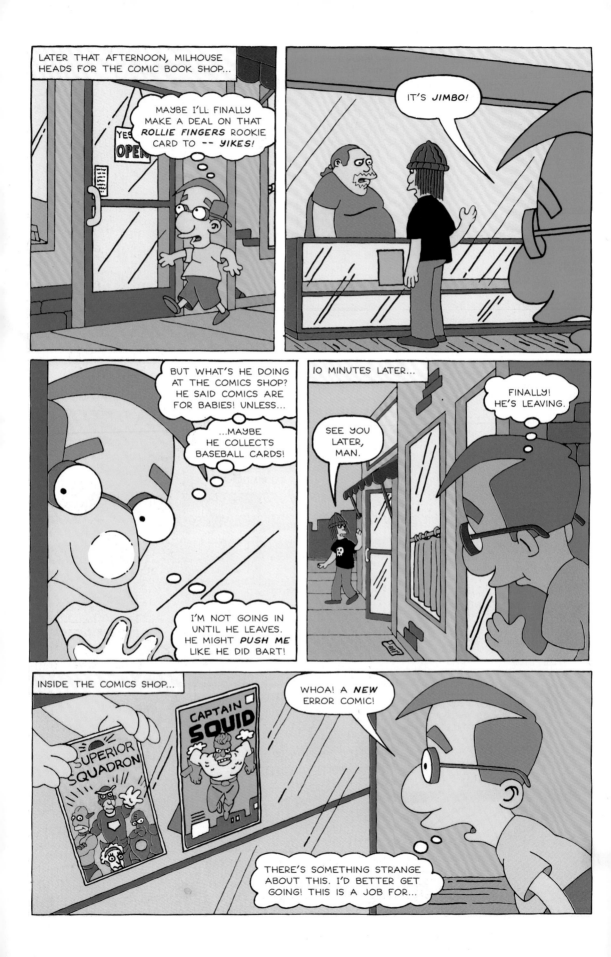

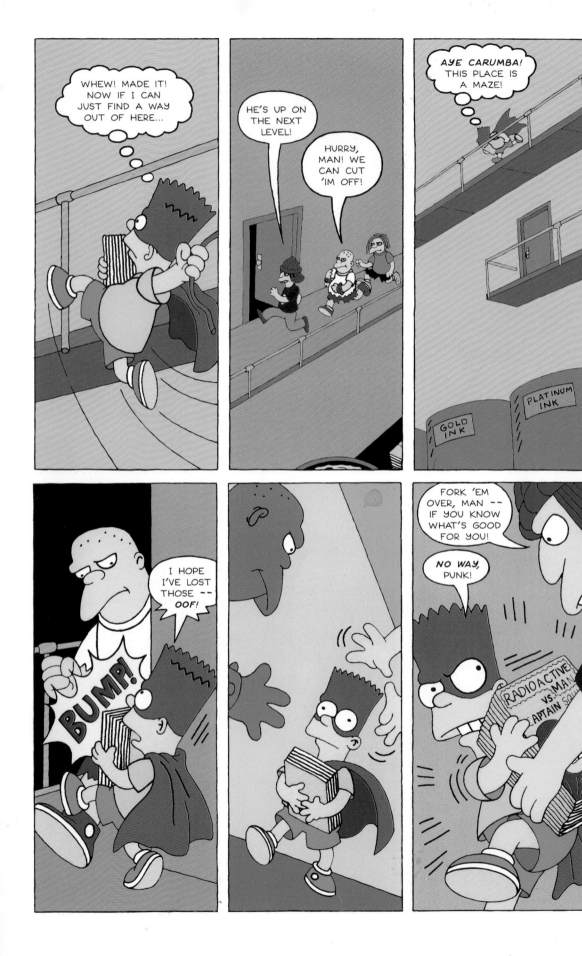

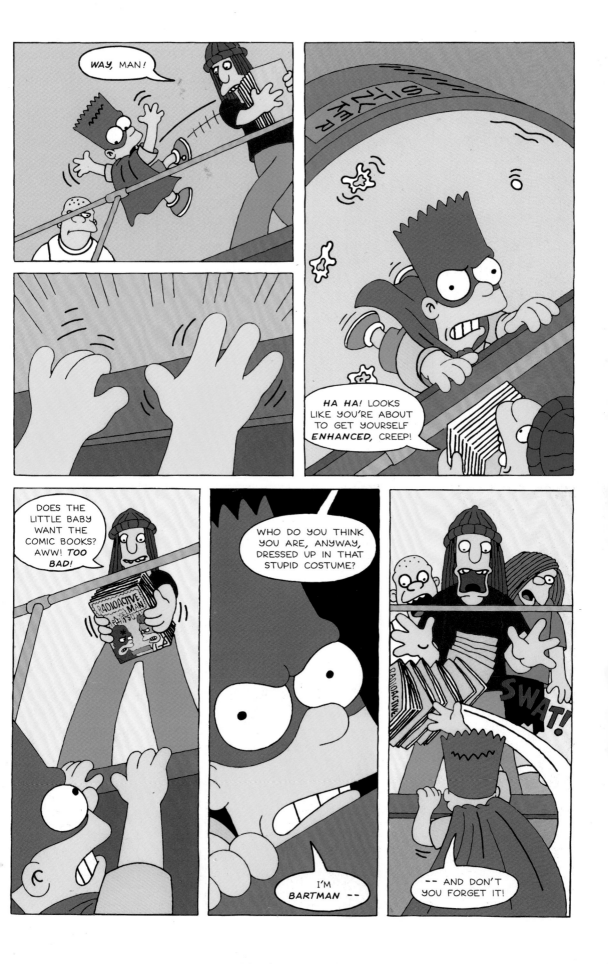

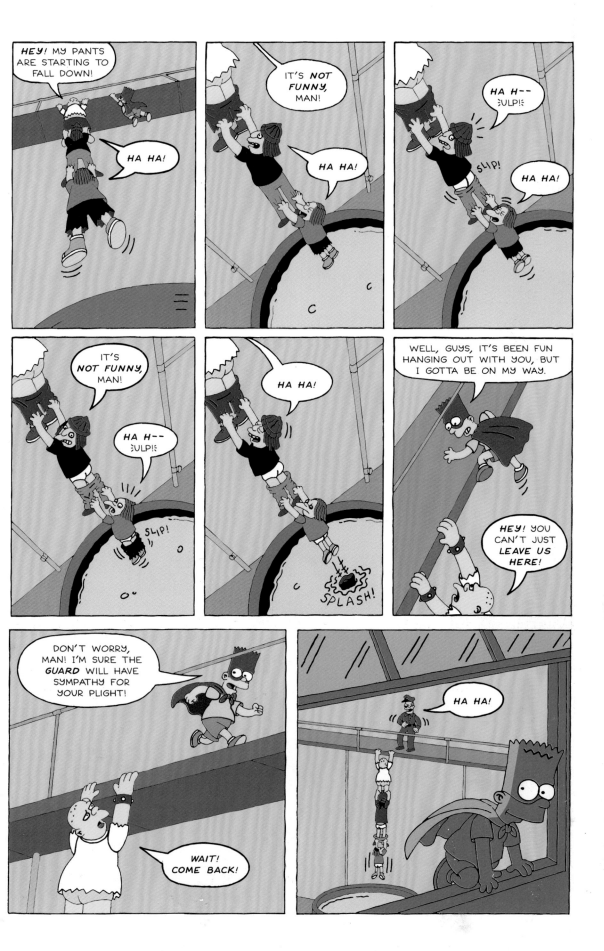

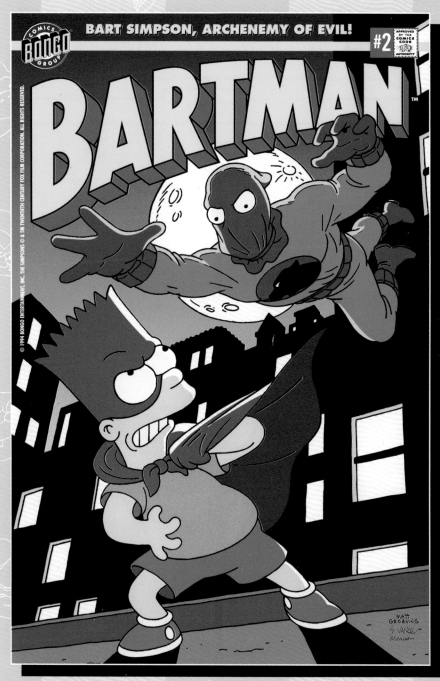

WHERE STALKS...
THE PENALIZER!

AN EVIL PRESENCE PROWLS SPRINGFIELD THIS NIGHT -- AND IT'S UP TO *BARTMAN* TO STOP HIM!

A MATT GROENING PRODUCTION

JAN STRNAD
SCRIPT

STEVE VANCE
PENCILS, EDITS

BILL MORRISON ☆ **TIM BAVINGTON** ☆ **PHIL ORTIZ**
FINISHED ART

CINDY VANCE
COLORS, EDITS

BARTMAN is published three times a year by Bongo Entertainment, Inc., 1999 Avenue of the Stars, Los Angeles, CA 90067. (310) 788-1367, Fax (310) 788-1200. Issue 2. ISSN #1073-9513. © 1994 Bongo Entertainment, Inc. The Simpsons © & TM Twentieth Century Fox Film Corporation. All rights reserved. Neither this comic book nor any portion of it may be used or reproduced for any purpose whatsoever without the express written permission of Bongo Entertainment, Inc. Stop reading this and get on with the story, man.
Printed on recycled paper with 10% post-consumer waste. PRINTED IN CANADA.

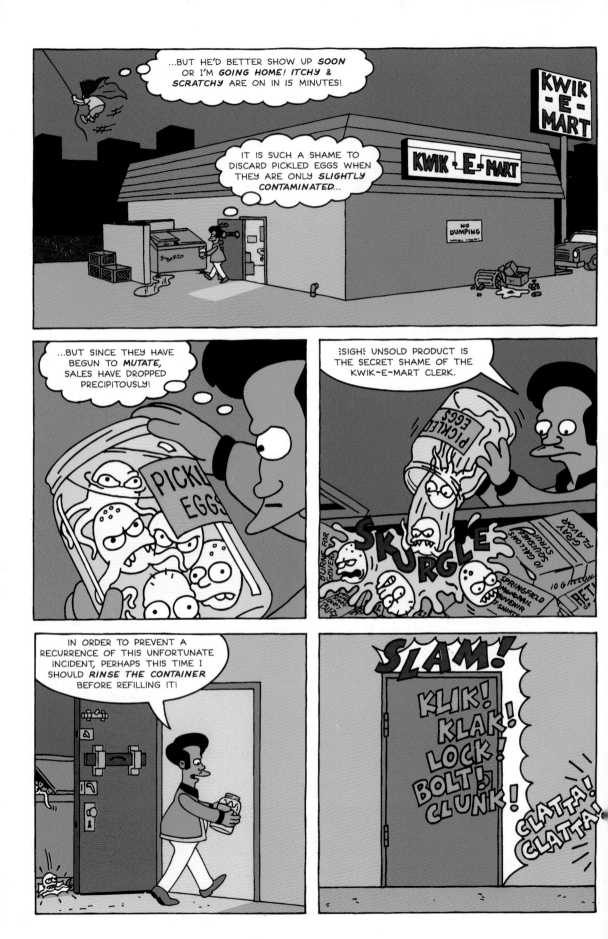

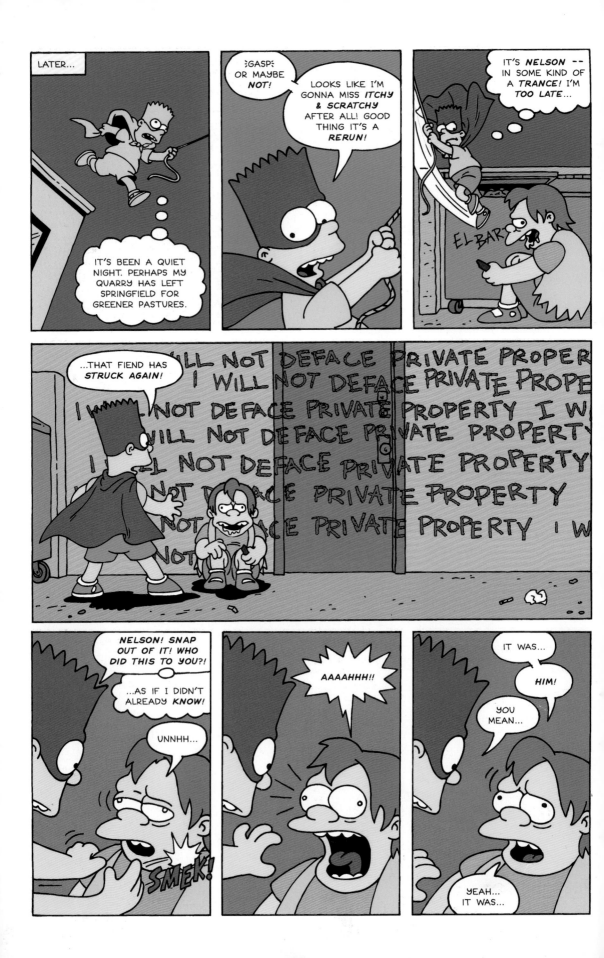

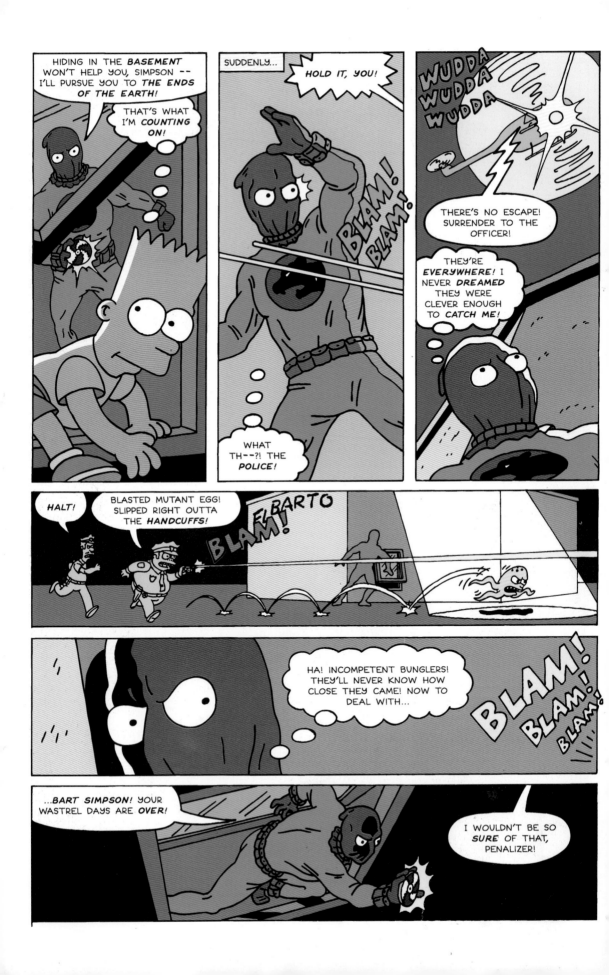

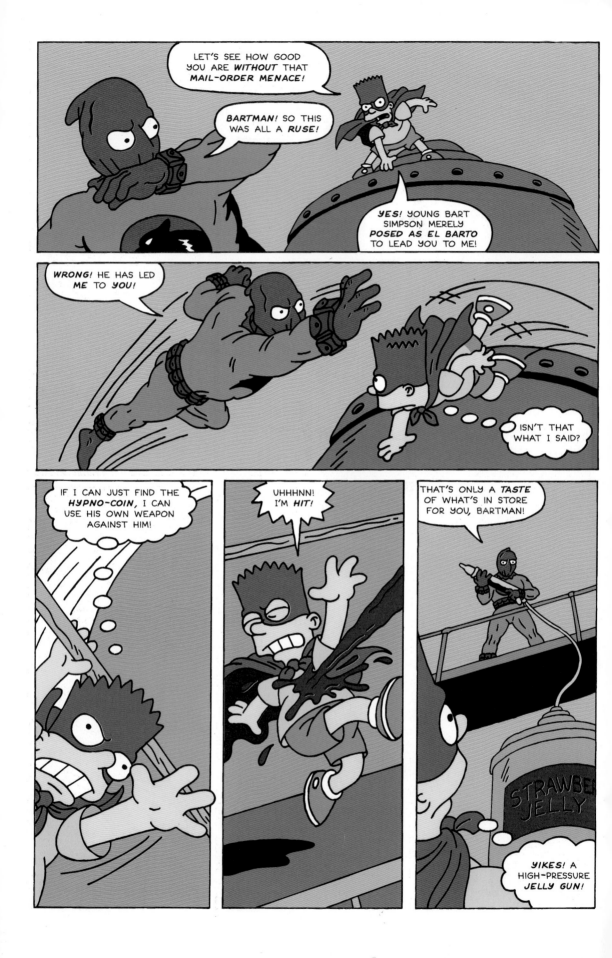

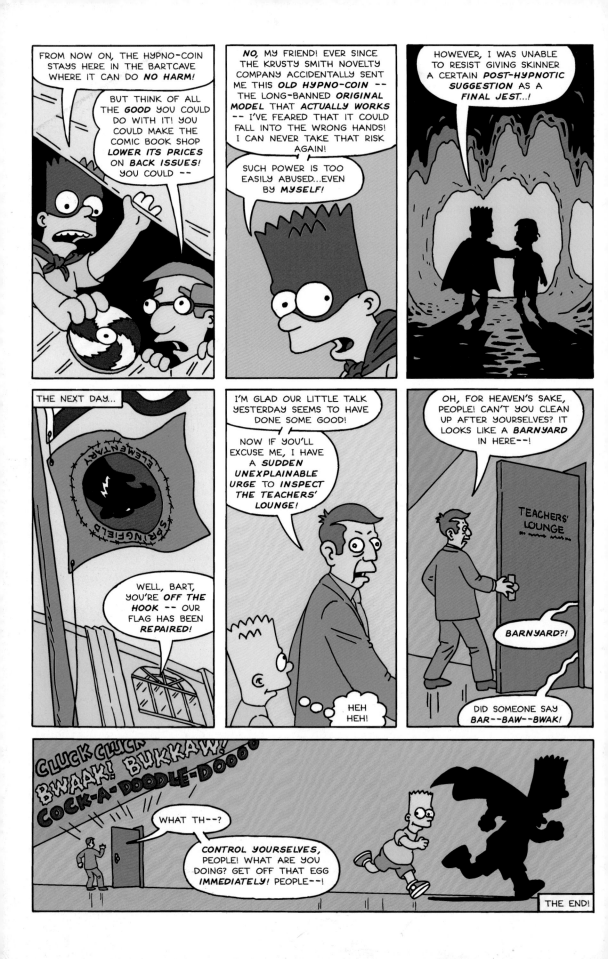

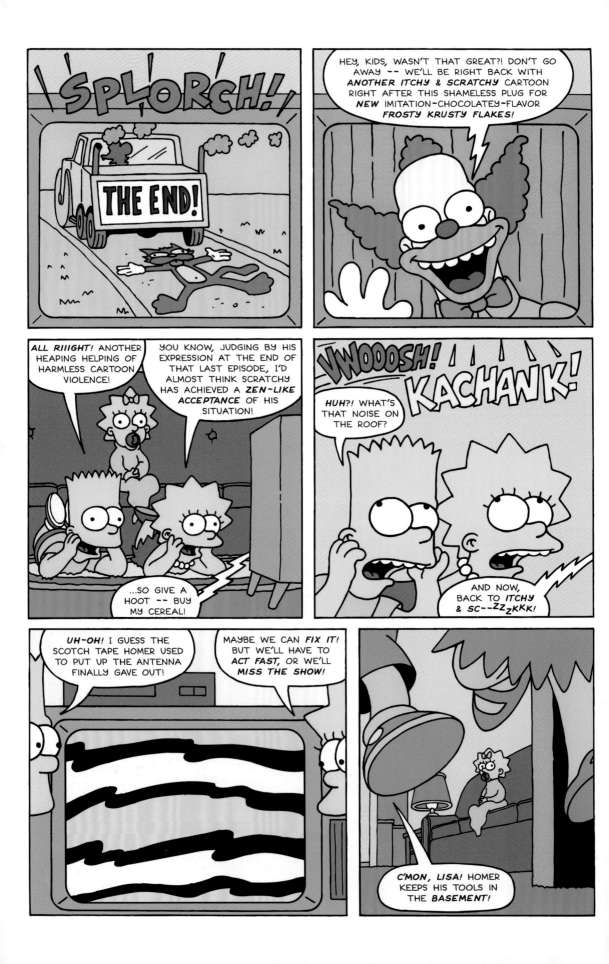

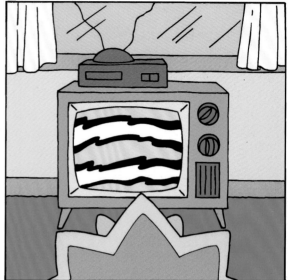

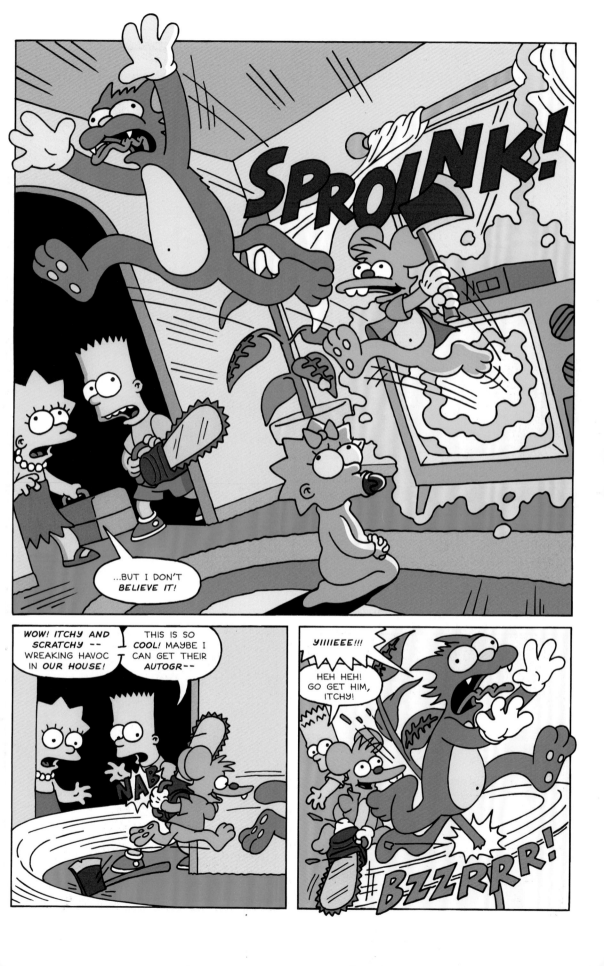

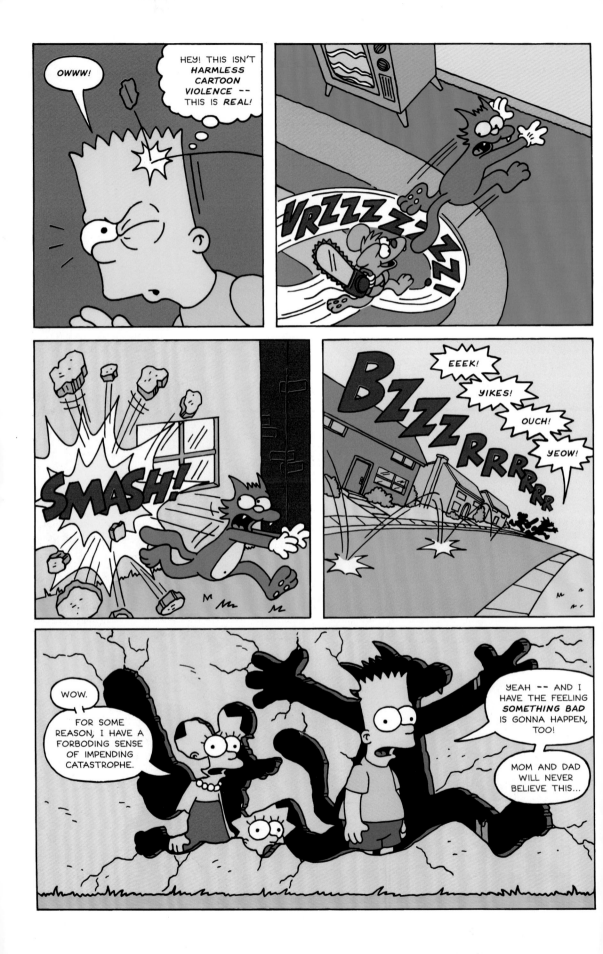

LATER...

:SIGH: I BET I'M THE **ONLY PERSON IN TOWN** WHO'S NOT GOING...

HEY--!

--IF EVERYBODY'S AT THE POWER PLANT, THAT MEANS JUST ONE THING! THIS BURG'S WIDE OPEN FOR...

...EL BARTO!

RAND | BRAND | BRAND | BRAN

PRAY AINT | SPRAY PAINT | SPRAY PAINT | SPR PAI

SOON...

--DILLY-DOODLY! *NOW* WE'RE ROLLING!

SILLY ME! GUESS I HAVEN'T GOTTEN THE HANG OF THIS NEW CAMCORDER -- I FORGOT TO FLIP THE OL' *"STANDBY"* SWITCHEROO!

STAND OVER THERE WITH YOUR MOM, KIDS -- I WANT TO GET A SHOT OF YOU IN FRONT OF THE STAGE-A-ROONY!

4TH ANNUAL ENERGY SQUANDERERS AWARDS AND

YO, NUKES COMEDY JAM

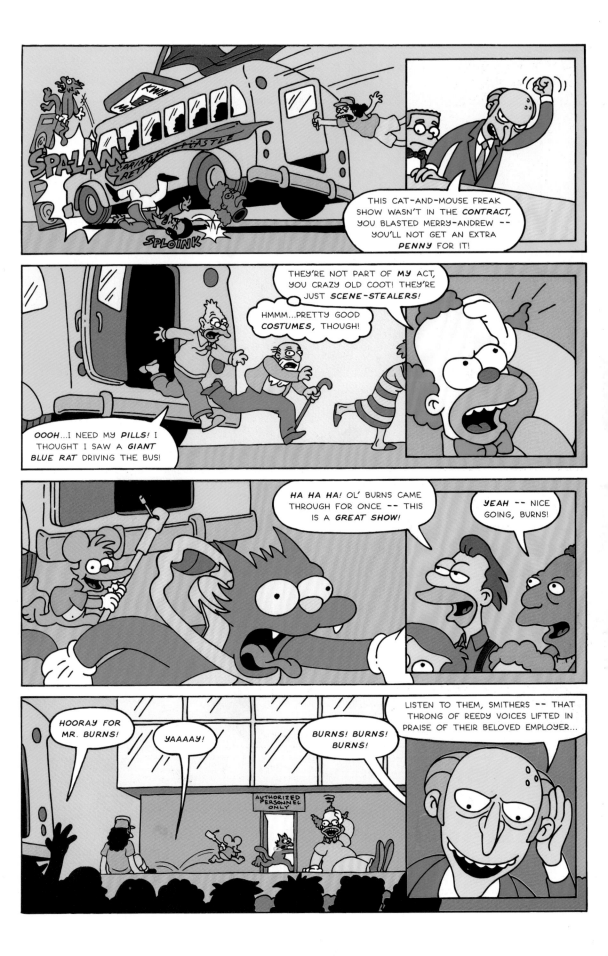

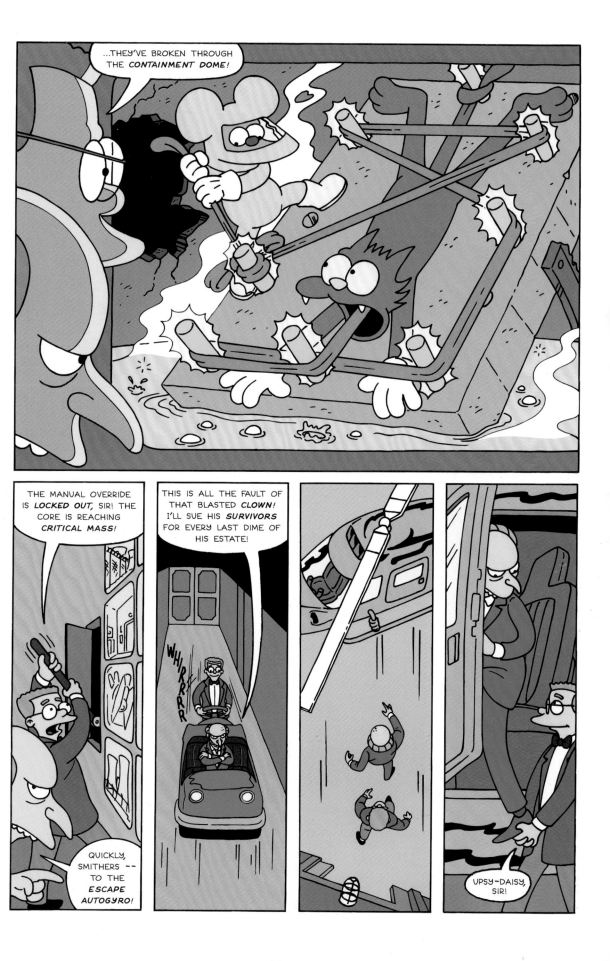

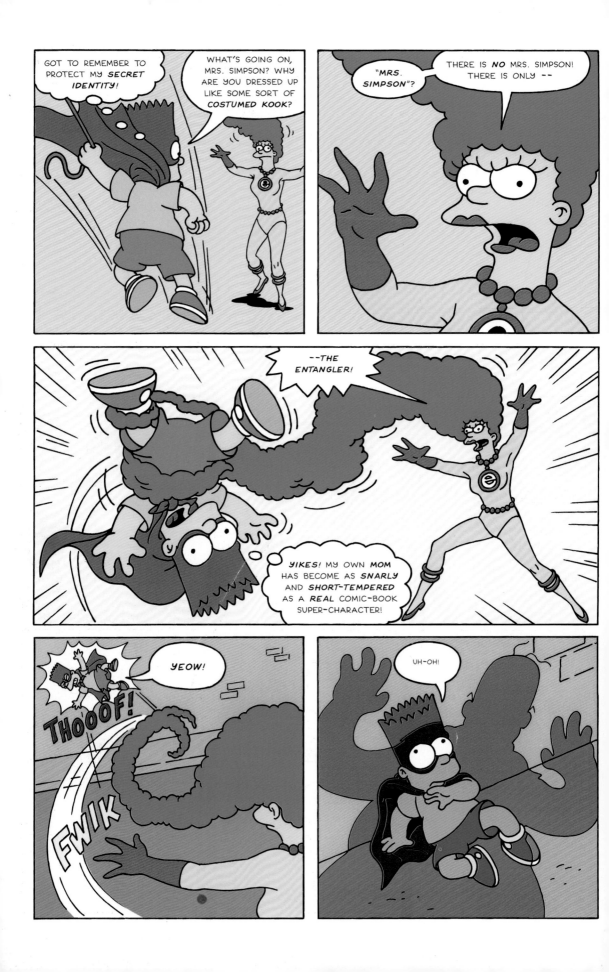

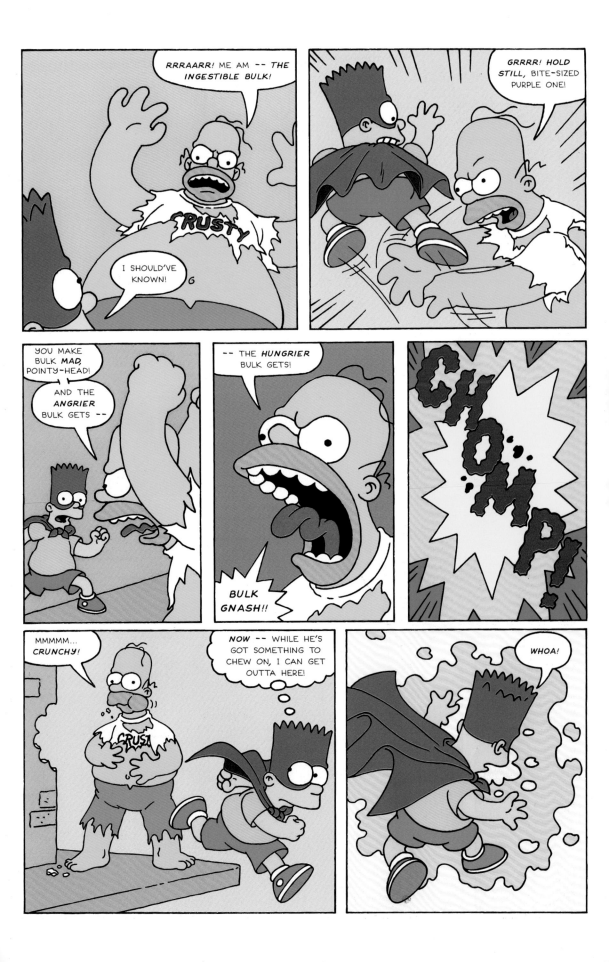

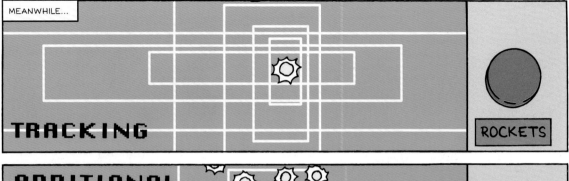

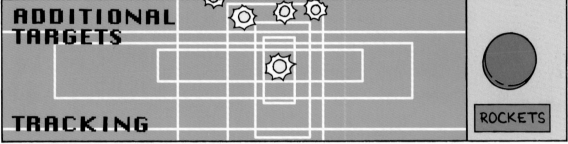

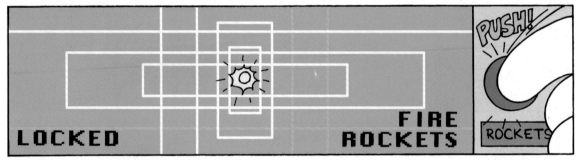

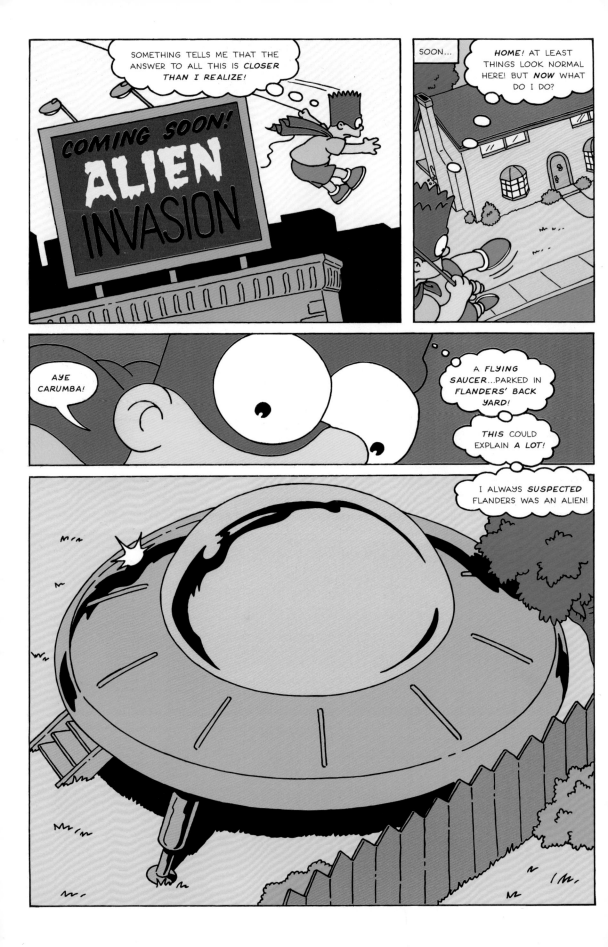

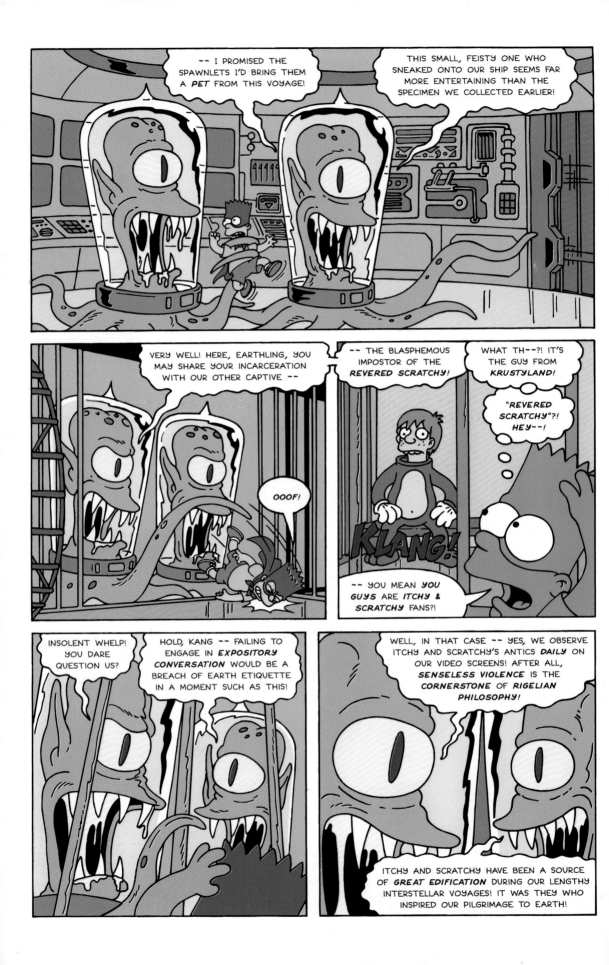

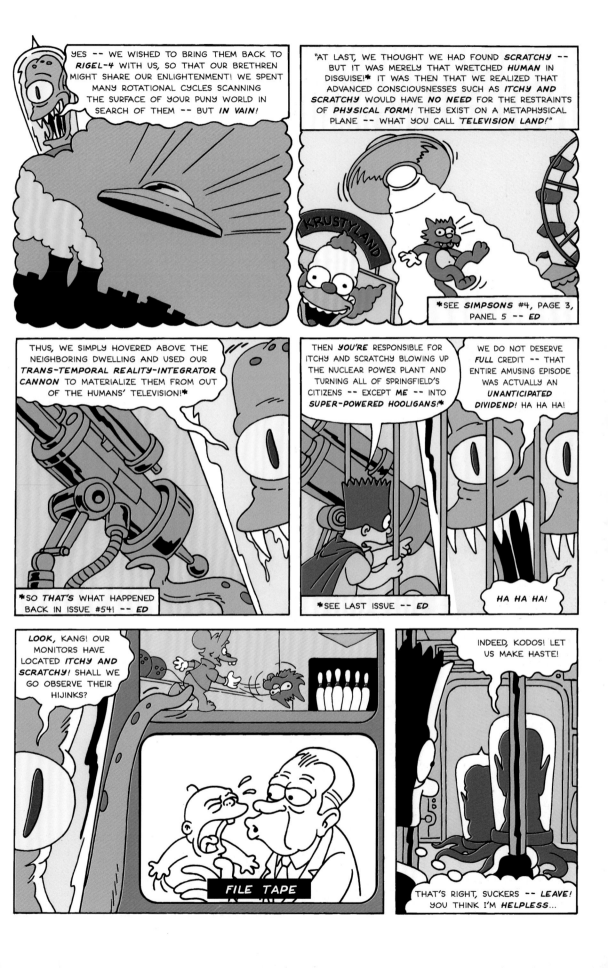

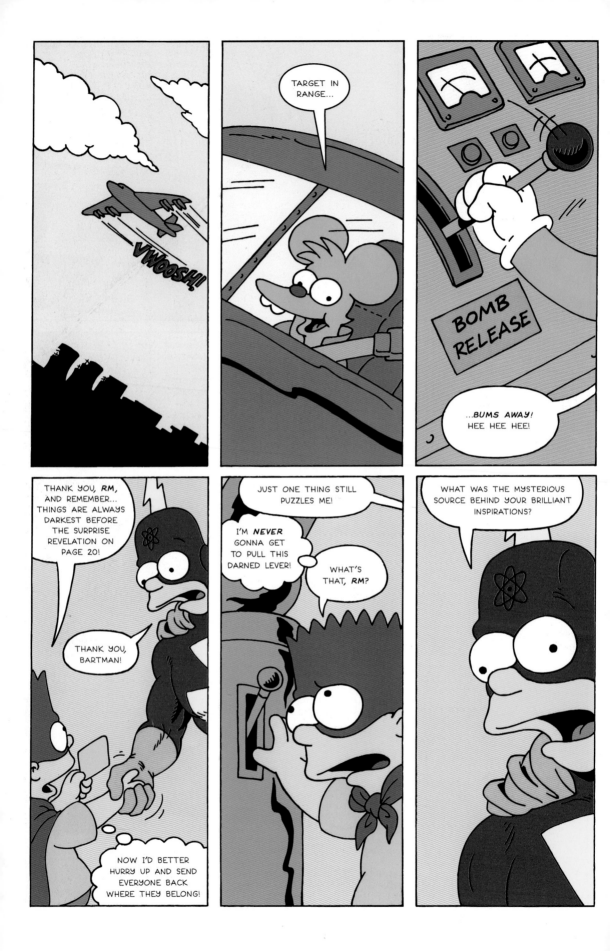

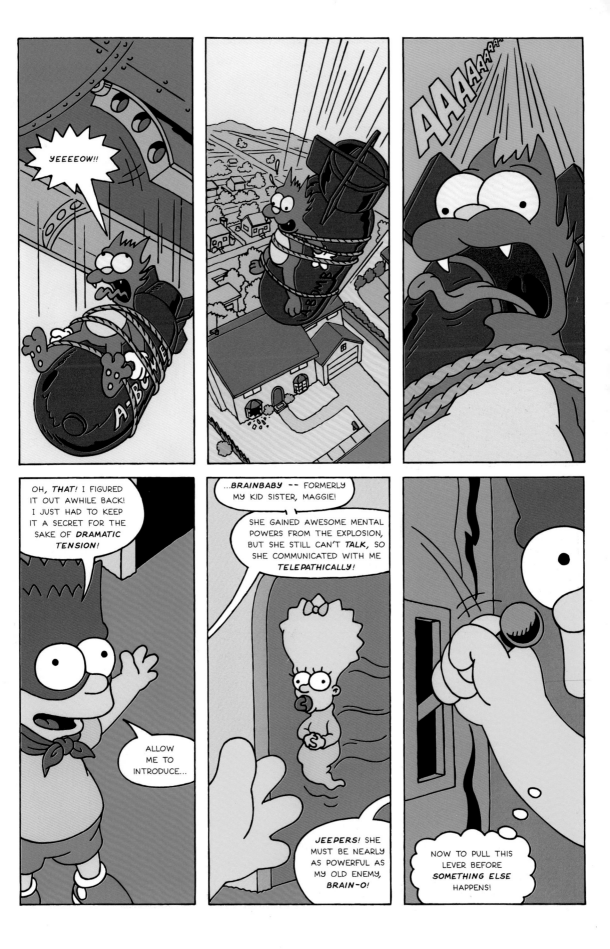

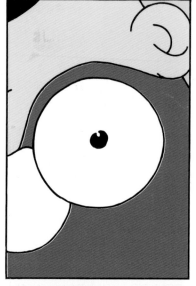

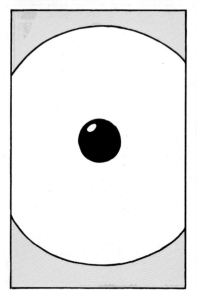
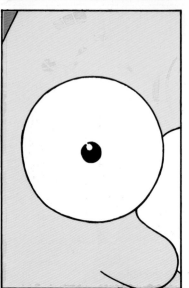

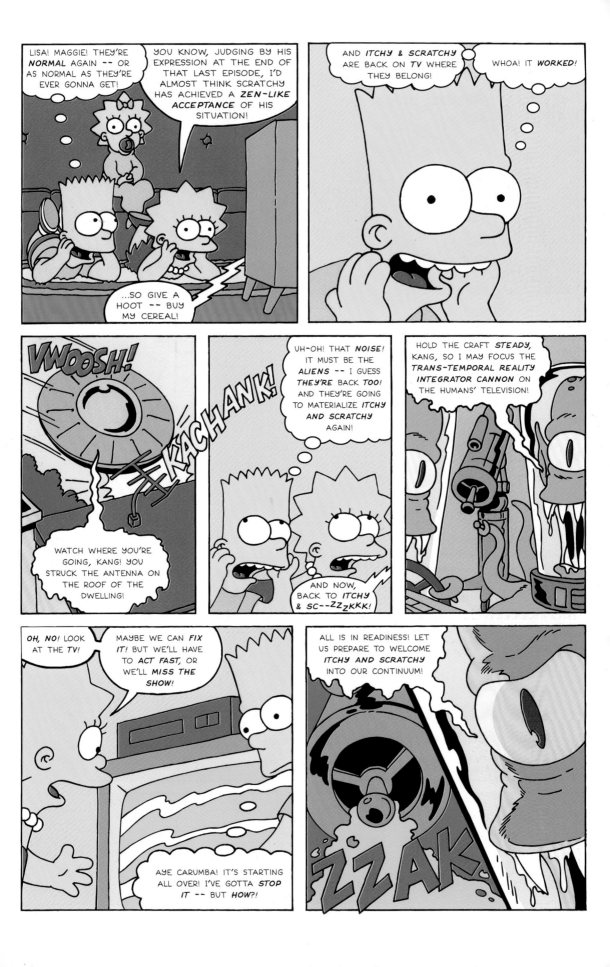

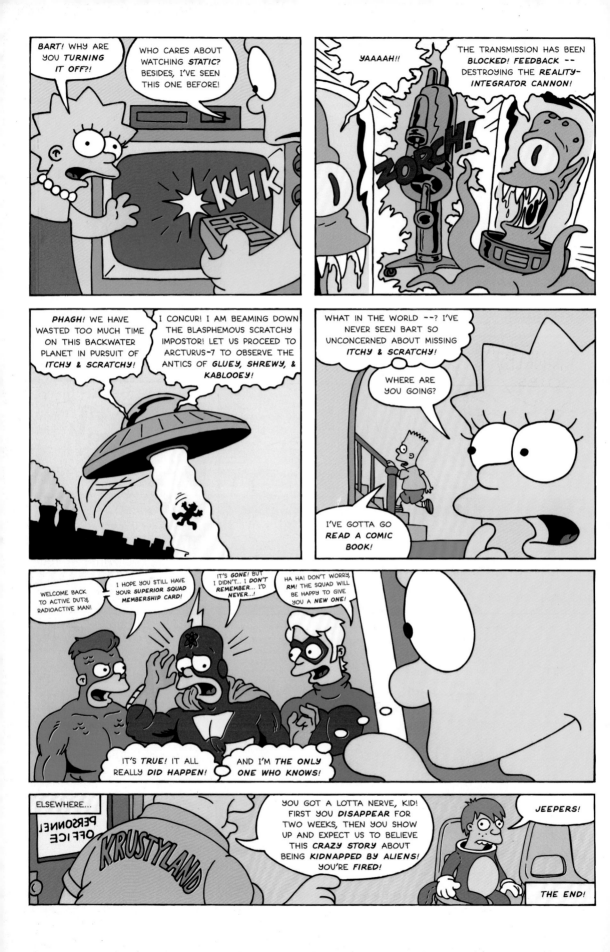

1. The Plaid Piper
2. Radioactive Man
3. Brainbaby
4. The Black Belch
5. The Jokester
6. Coma
7. Barfly
8. The Mudslinger
9. The Jazzler
10. Simpleton

11. The Penalizer
12. Bartman
13. Vampiredna
14. The Ingestible Bulk
15. Piggum
16. The Entangler
17,19. The Mirror Maidens
18. The Scarlet Whimpernel